Pre-K Thinking Skills

W9-CTG-538

Dear Parents:

Your preschool child will develop key thinking skills by completing the enjoyable, colourful activities in this workbook. Comparing, classifying, counting, sequencing, matching, colours, analogies, and more are taught using Canadian themes.

For each page, we suggest reading the directions aloud to your child and talking together about the solved example. Encourage your child to work through the activity independently but be ready to provide a little help when needed. You can support your child's learning by showing enthusiasm for their effort, keeping each session relaxed, and changing activities when your child shows signs of tiring.

Above all, enjoy this special time with your child!

Sincerely,

The *Thinking Skills* Team

Contents

Canadian Curriculum Press is an imprint of Telegraph Road.
©2017 Telegraph Road
ISBN 978-1-4876-0292-5

Alice Prendergast
Senior Series Editor: Lisa Penttila
Series and Cover Design: Michael P. Brodey
Selected Illustrations: Andrea Scobie

For special bulk purchases please contact:
sales@telegraph-rd.com

For other inquiries please contact:
inquiries@telegraph-rd.com

We acknowledge the financial support of the Government of Canada through the Canada Book Fund (CBF) for our publishing activities.

 Canadian Heritage   Patrimoine canadien

Printed in Canada

Same and Different

Circle the picture in each row that is **different**.

Same and Different

Circle the picture in each row that is **different**.

  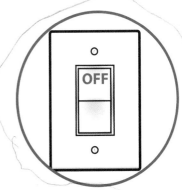 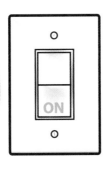

Same and Different

Colour the pictures that are the **same**.

Same and Different

Colour the picture that is **different**.

Bigger and Smaller

Visit the zoo in Vancouver!

Circle the animal in each row that is **bigger** than the others.

Bigger and Smaller

The band is playing in the Calgary concert hall!
Circle the instrument in each row that is **smaller** than the others.

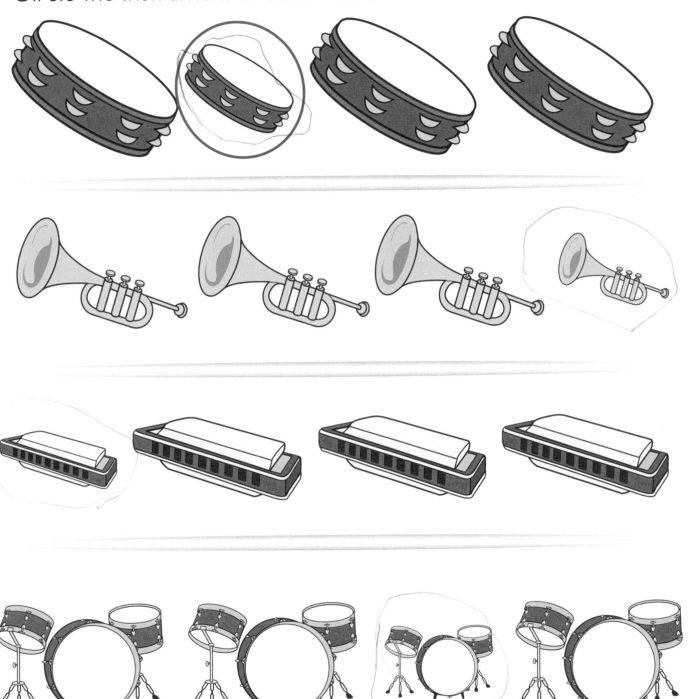

Bigger and Smaller

Lily loves lemons! Circle all the **bigger** lemons. Put an X on all the **smaller** lemons.

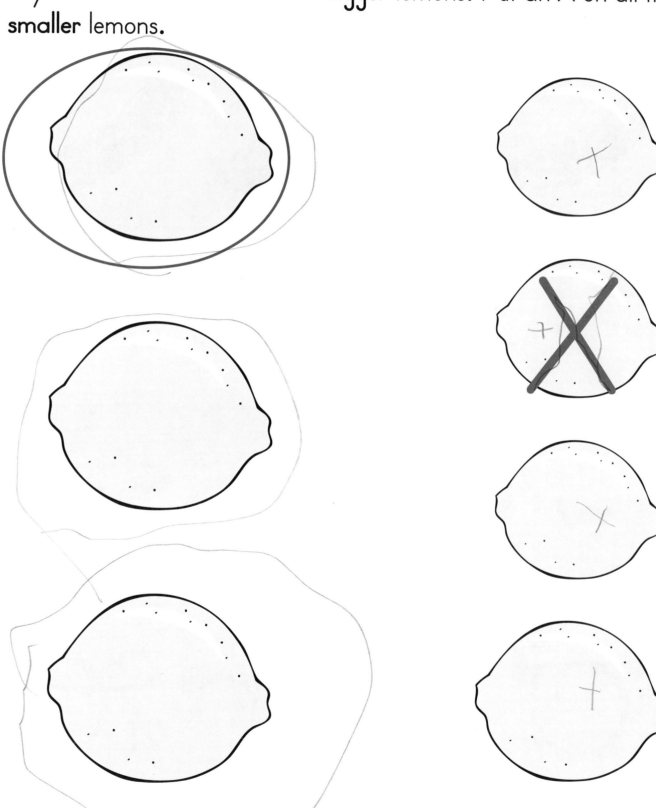

What Goes Together?

Draw a line from each worker to the item he or she needs.

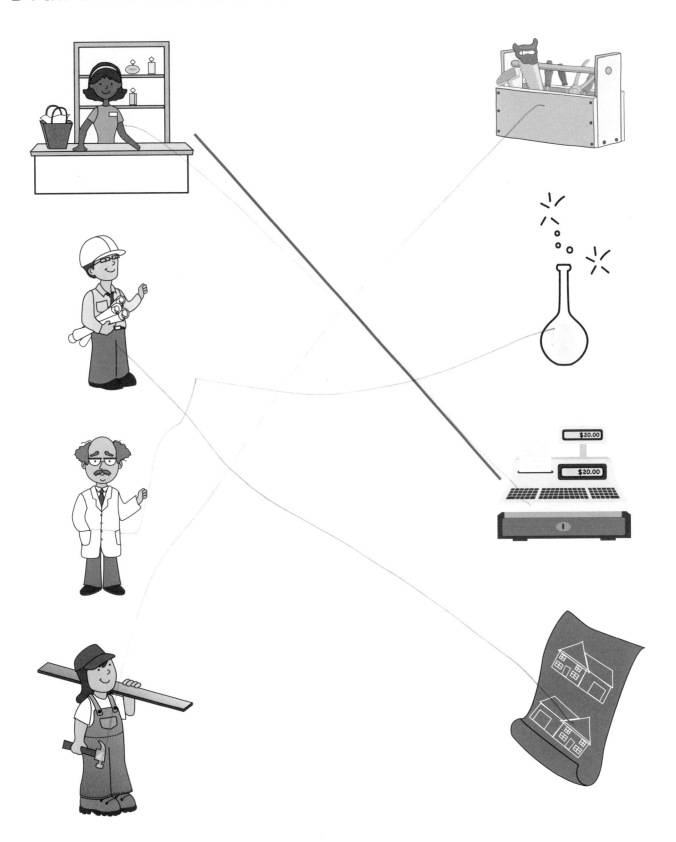

What Goes Together?

Draw a line from each worker to the item he or she needs.

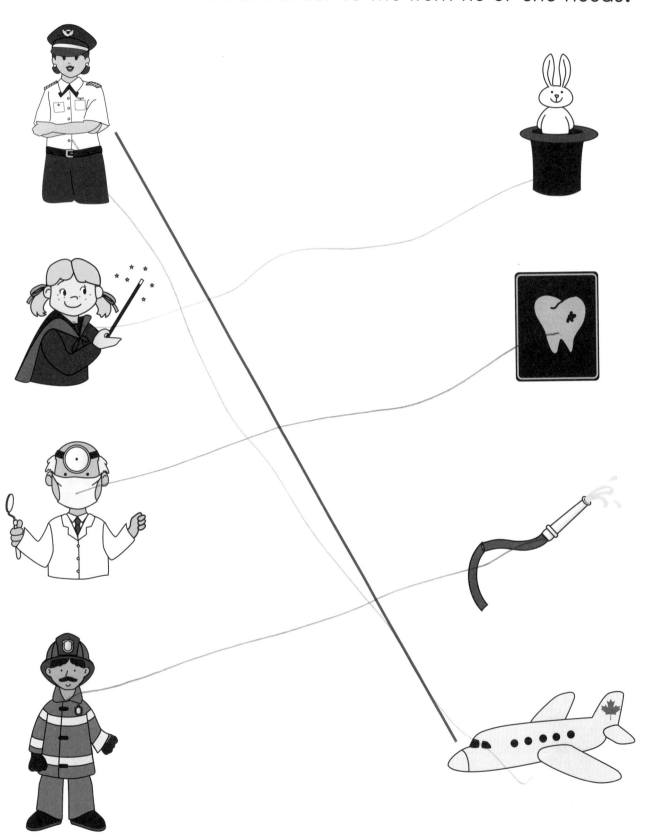

First, Next, Last

Use yellow to circle what happened **first.** Use blue to circle what happened **next.** Use red to circle what happened **last.**

First, Next, Last

Use blue to circle what happened **first in the spring.** Use yellow to circle what happened **next in the summer.** Use red to circle what happened **last in the fall.**

Above and Below

Colour the fish **above** the waves green. Colour the fish **below** the waves red.

Matching Shapes

Circle the shape that is the same as the first one in the row.
Say the name of each shape.

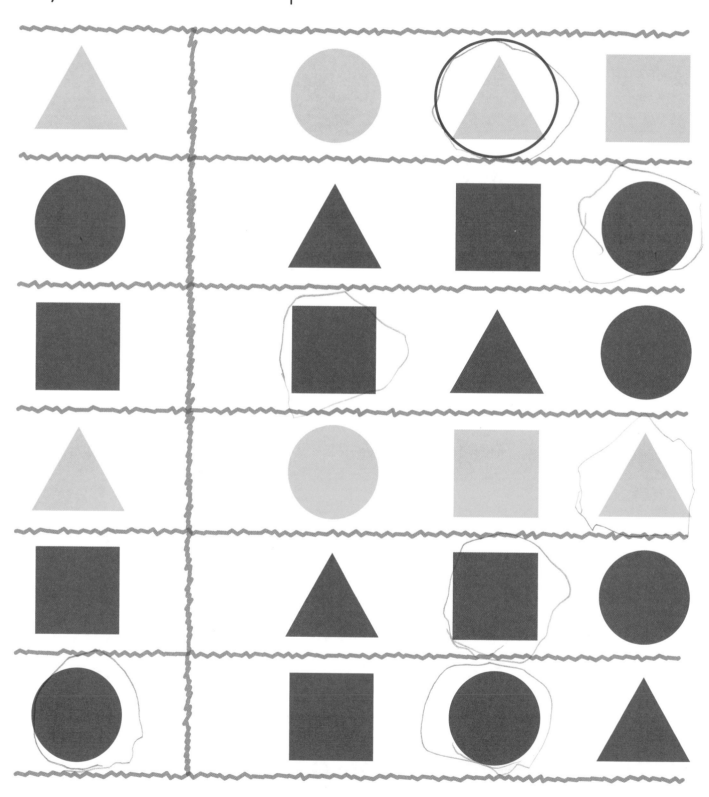

Matching Shapes

Draw a line to connect matching shapes. Say the name of each shape.

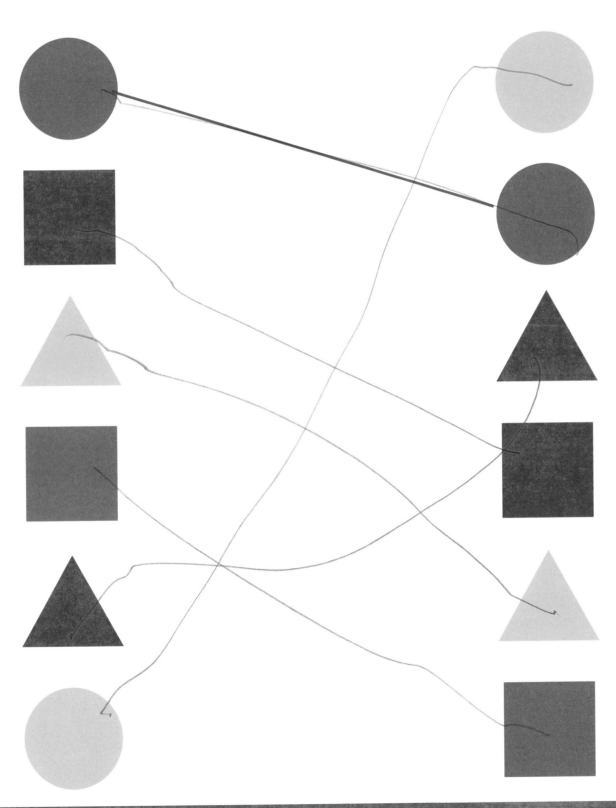

Perfect Patterns

Circle what comes next in each pattern.

Perfect Patterns

Circle what comes next in each pattern.

Same Order

Circle the row of pictures that is in the same order as the top one.

Different Order

Put an X on the row of pictures that is in a different order from the top one.

Jumbled Up Jobs

Circle with a blue crayon the things that the veterinarian might see. Circle with a red crayon the things that the chef might see.

Jumbled Up Jobs

Circle with a blue crayon the things that the conductor might see.
Circle with a red crayon the things that the letter carrier might see.

Categories

Circle everything that can fly. Put an **X** on everything that has wheels. How many things can fly **and** have wheels?

Categories

Circle everything that floats. Put an X on everything that is red. How many things can float **and** are red?

Analogy

Think about how  and go together. The is for wearing on the . Circle what goes with in the same way.

Think about how and go together. Circle what goes with in the same way.

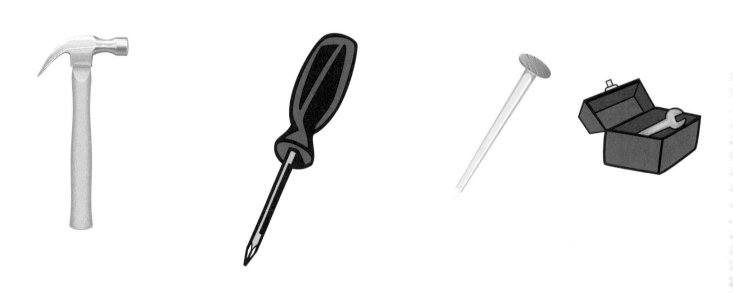

Analogy

Think about how  and ⬜ go together. Circle what goes with 🏀 in the same way.

Think about how 🦋 and 🐛 go together. Circle what goes with 🐸 in the same way.

Analogy

Think about how the first pair of things goes together. Circle another pair of things that go together in the same way.

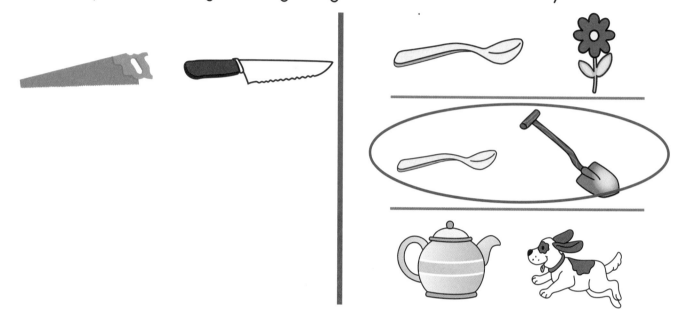

Think about how the first pair of things goes together. Circle **another pair** of things that go together in the same way.

Analogy

Think about how the first pair of things goes together. Circle other **pairs** of things that go together in the same way.

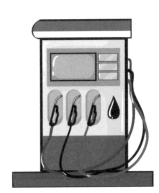

Most and Fewest

Heather went birdwatching in Halifax. Here is what she saw. Circle what she saw the **most** of. Underline what she saw the **fewest** of.

Most and Fewest

Ted is tidying up his bedroom in Toronto. This is what he found. Circle what he found the **most** of. Underline what he found the **fewest** of.

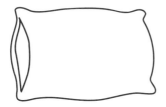

Crazy Colours

Circle the items that are the incorrect colour.

Crazy Colours

Circle the items that are the incorrect colour.

Matching Pictures

Draw a line from each picture on the left to the matching picture on the right.

Matching Pictures

Draw a line from each picture on the left to the matching picture on the right.

Matching Pictures

Draw a line from each item on the left to a different item on the right that is the same colour.

Matching Pictures

Draw a line from each item on the left to a different item on the right that is the same colour.

Colour the Shapes

Colour the circles yellow. Colour the triangles brown. Colour the squares blue.

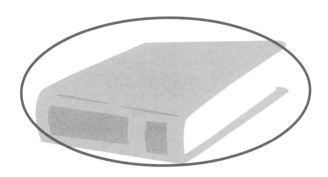

Stack and Roll

Circle the things that can be stacked. Put an X on the things that can roll. How many things can be stacked **and** roll?

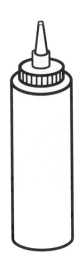

Following Instructions

Put a red circle on things **on** the table that are good to eat. Put a blue X on things **under** the table that you can wear. Put a green square on things **beside** the table that are nice to hug.

Following Instructions

Put a red circle on things **on** the tent that can fly. Put a blue X on things **on** the log that can jump. Put a green square on things **beside** the tent that are green.

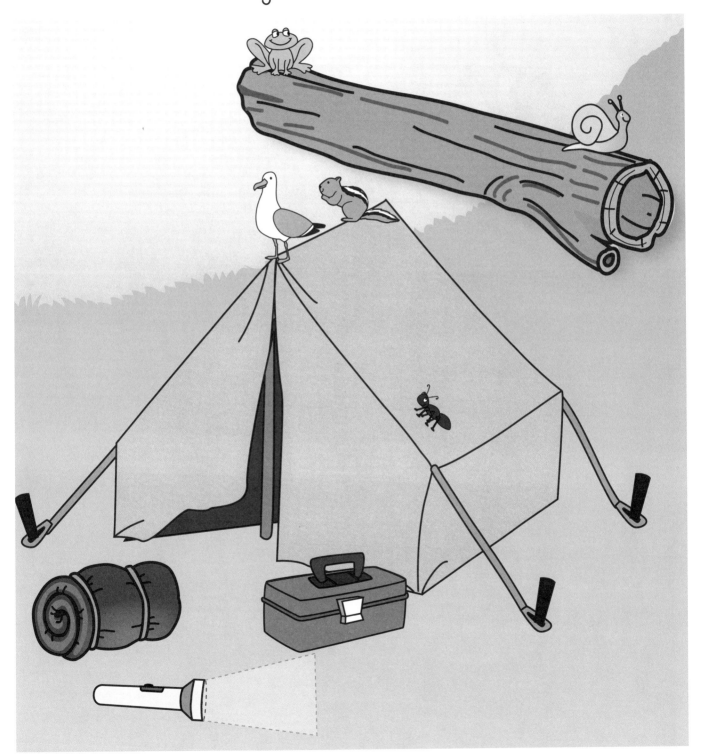

Music Maze

Draw a line to help the conductor find the instrument that is played by hitting it.

Music Maze

Now help the conductor find the instrument that is played by blowing into it.

Counting

Ben the Beaver, Molly the Moose, Cathy the Caribou and Gordon the Grizzly Bear want to go canoeing. Circle enough lifejackets for all of the animals.

Count the Items

Draw a line from the number to the matching group of items.

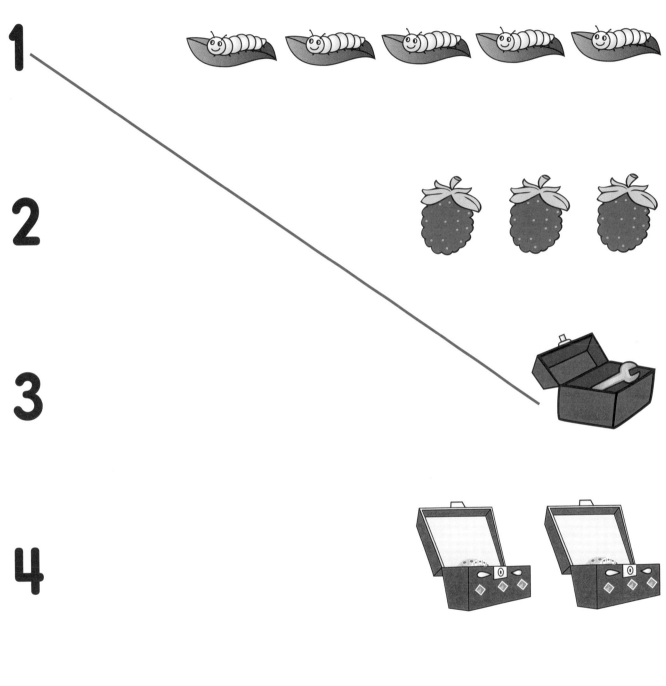

1

2

3

4

5

Thinking Skills

More and Fewer

Count the items in each set. Circle the set that has **fewer** in each row.

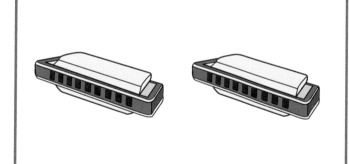 

 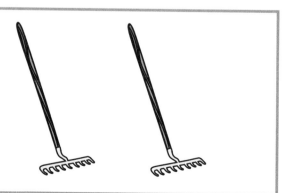

Thinking Skills

More and Fewer

Count the items in each set. Circle the set that has **more** in each row.

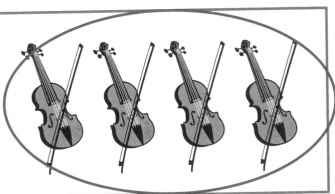

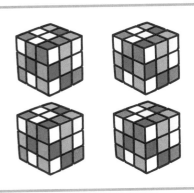
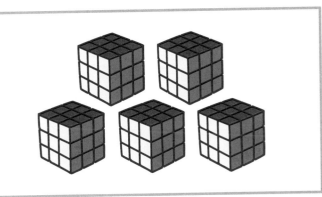

Jumbled Up Jobs

Carl the Construction Worker is at the construction site. Wendy the Waitress is at the diner. Draw a line from each worker to the items he or she might see at work.

Jumbled Up Jobs

Zoe the Zookeeper is at the zoo. Simon the Sales Clerk is at the furniture store. Draw a line from each worker to the items he or she might see at work.

Crazy Kitchen

Circle things that belong in a kitchen.

Cluttered Classroom

Put an X on things that **don't** belong in a classroom.

Thinking Skills

Left and Right

Circle animals that are looking to the **right**.

Hint: left    right

Left and Right

Circle animals that are looking to the **left**.

Hint: left  → right

Counting

Count the friends at the party. Circle the number of cake slices needed so everyone can have one slice.

Rainy Day

Count the people in the family. Circle the number of umbrellas needed so everyone can have one. Who is too young to hold an umbrella?

Opposites Attract

Draw a line from each picture to its opposite.

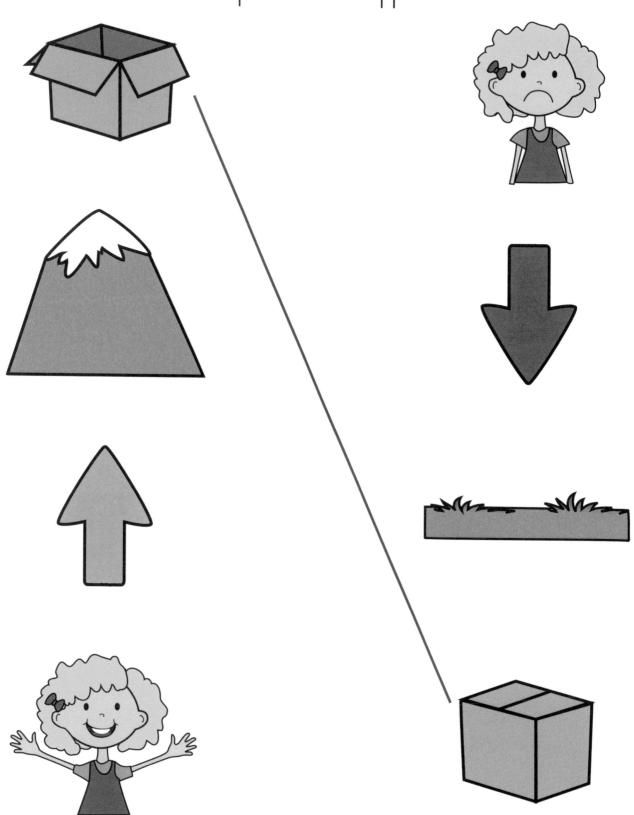

Opposites Attract

Draw a line from each picture to its opposite.

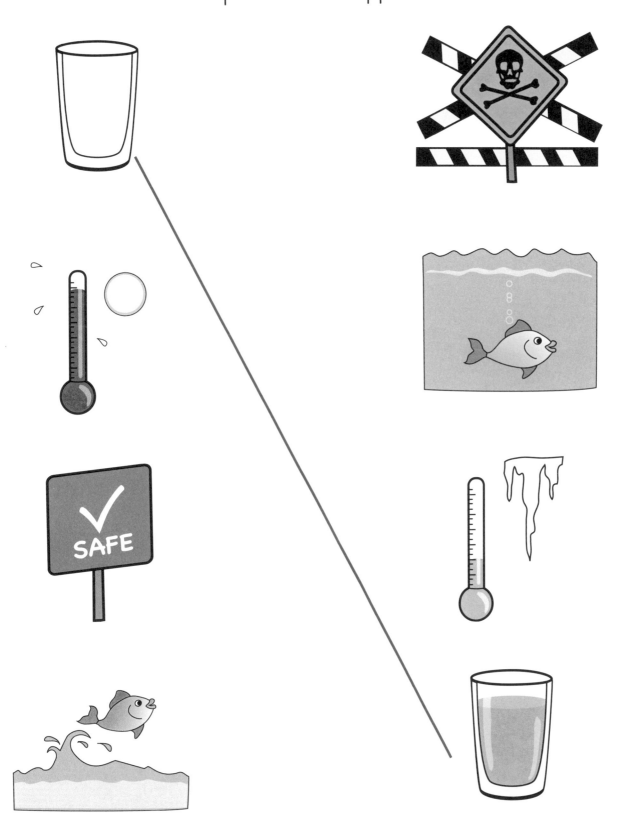

SAFE

Shadow Sorting

Draw a line from the item to its shadow.

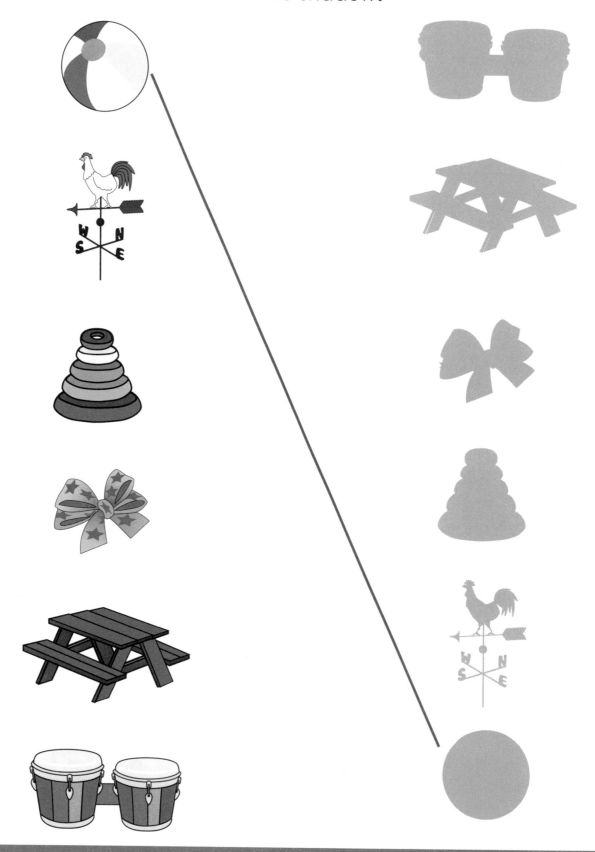

Rabbit Maze!

Help Robby Rabbit find what he likes to eat.

Draw a Picture

Draw a picture of your favourite animal. Then draw what it likes to eat.

Colouring and Sorting

Use brown to colour the animal that has fur. Use red to colour the animal with feathers. Use green to colour the animal that moves slowly.

Sorting

Kate and Kai are going grocery shopping in Kitchener. Circle the items they might see on the way to the store.

Sorting

Glen is gardening in Gaspé. Put an X on the items that he does *not* need.

Sorting

Put a red circle on animals that you might see in a barn. Put a blue circle on things that are vegetables.

Sorting

Put a black X on things that you would **not** see in the kitchen.

Canadian Dot-to-Dot

Complete the dot-to-dot maze to draw the symbol on the Canadian flag. Colour the symbol red. What is it?

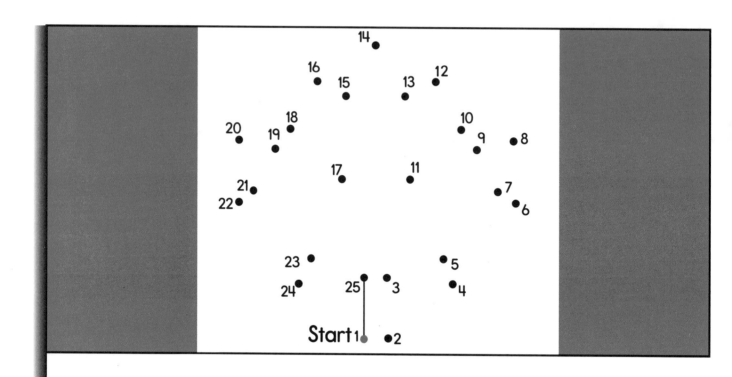